It Will Take a Lot of Force to Give the HEIMLICH to a Horse

Ringtail Learning
San Francisco

By Mister Lemur

IT WILL TAKE A LOT OF FORCE
TO GIVE THE HEIMLICH TO A HORSE

By Mister Lemur

Copyright 2017
by Hans & Jen Hartvickson
Printed in the United States of America
First Edition, 2017

Published by
Ringtail Learning,
San Francisco, CA

ISBN: 978-0-9828866-7-0

Library of Congress Control Number: 2016950028

To explore more of The Scheming Lemurs' world, visit www.MisterLemur.com

This book is available at a quantity discount when purchased for educational use.
Contact misterlemur@misterlemur.com

Mister Lemur is a trademark of Hans Hartvickson.

Heimlich Maneuver® is a registered service mark of The Heimlich Institute and is used by
permission.

Thank you to Amy Bauman and Mimi Lemur for their editorial insight,
and 'ideasforu' for awesome illustrations.

PLEASE NOTE: *This book is designed to help readers become aware of the importance
of learning first aid and to make readers laugh. These are NOT proper instructions for
the Heimlich Maneuver, and this book is NOT to be taken as guidance on steps to take
in an emergency. This book does not in any way constitute medical advice. We encourage
everyone to consider taking part in a first-aid class that includes age-appropriate
Heimlich techniques, such as Heimlich Heroes™. Horse owners, please consult with your
veterinarian for proper horse first-aid techniques. To our knowledge, the Heimlich
Maneuver has not been shown to be an effective way to save a choking horse.*

To

first responders

of all ages

This is a story about my sister, Lemur Pup, who was able to save her horse because she had learned first aid.

Through an old wooden fence,
I observed my sweet mare
as she tried without luck
to get breaths of fresh air.

When I looked I could see
that her throat was blocked with . . .

"Oh, my goodness! She's choked on a green Granny Smith!"

Granny Smith: A type of green apple, commonly used for cooking

It was not the whole apple,
but simply one half,
and I hoped I could free it
by making her laugh.
So I picked up a feather
and tickled her knees . . .

4

I did all that I could
to inspire a sneeze . . .

I showed her my silliest, funniest face . . .

I spurred her with spurs
as if starting a race.

And when none of that worked,
the next thing that I tried
was to see if my fingers
could sweep it aside.

But my arm could not reach!
I looked down in despair.
Then I saw a small fruit-worm
was wriggling there!

9

So I asked that green worm,
"Would you please help us bore
a small hole to let air
through the Granny Smith's core?"

bore: to make a hole or tunnel

"It's your natural skill!
You just do what you do!
You will soon make a hole
for the air to pass through!"

But the worm, he just wriggled,
as if to say, "No . . .
we must think of a plan
that is fast and not slow!"

11

With each moment that passed,
there was more and more need
to come up with a plan
that would get the chunk freed.

Then I thought to myself,
"You have been first-aid trained!"
And I pictured that nurse,
in my class, who'd explained . . .

HEIMLICH MANEUVER

all the steps that you take
to solve problems like these
with the Heimlich Maneuver,
a lifesaving squeeze.

So I took a deep breath
and thought back on that course,
and I started the Heimlich
on my choking horse!

But through trial and error
and testing I found
that my horse was too large.
I could not reach around!

So I pulled out the rope
that was coiled on my hip,
and I cinched her up tight
so the rope would not slip.

Then I fashioned a pulley
attached to a stone,
and I pushed on that rock
with a grunt and a groan.

17

But the plan I'd devised
did not help my poor friend.
It just made her head hurt,
and it made the tree bend!

By a stroke of good luck,
a small group had walked by.
"Help me rescue my horse!
Or at least help me try!"

So, we all joined our arms,
and we clinched them quite tight,
set to give her the Heimlich
with all of our might.

When we found the right spot,
we all counted to three,
then a squeeze, and a lift . . .
and the apple popped free!

She looked up at our group,
through big, watery eyes,
and she whinnied, "I hope
that you all realize

what a difference your training
and quick thinking made.
You're all heroes today
because you learned first aid."

Then I gave her a hug,
and I went on my way,
and this story is why
I can stand here and say . . .

24

It will take a lot of force
to give the Heimlich to a horse!

25

The Heimlich Can Help
With Dr. Stephen Long

When something is stuck in a person's throat, preventing air from entering the lungs, we say the person is "choking." Our lungs need frequent breaths of fresh air – about one breath every three to six seconds – and this choking, or blockage of air, is a big problem if not stopped quickly.

Did you know?

- The Heimlich Maneuver is named after Henry Heimlich, an American doctor who invented the procedure in 1974.

- Henry's wife, Jane, was a writer, and she authored two books.

- The Heimlich Maneuver is credited with saving more than 100,000 lives.

- In 2016, at age 96, Henry used the Heimlich Maneuver to save the life of a dining companion who was choking.

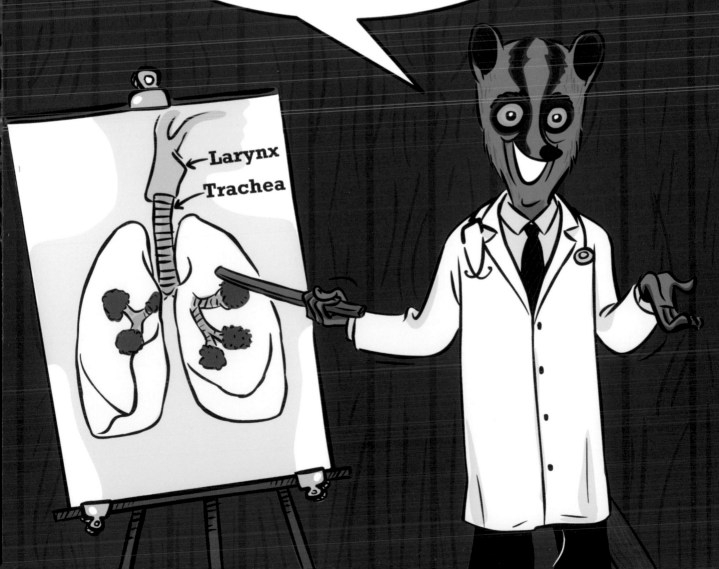

ABOUT THE AUTHORS

Hans Hartvickson has been writing stories and poems since he was in first grade. He loves sharing the fun of rhyming stories with kids of all ages.

Hans holds a bachelor's degree in economics from Stanford University and an M.B.A. from The University of Pennsylvania's Wharton School.

A ring-tailed lemur whispers a story idea to Hans.

Jen Hartvickson travels the country speaking to schools, art associations, and after-school programs about the importance of writing, setting goals, and making plans.

Jen earned a bachelor's degree in sociology and a master's degree in education from Stanford University.

Jen shares her love of writing with students.

Doctor Stephen Long is a pediatric anesthesiologist at UCSF Benioff Children's Hospital in Oakland, California. Two of his favorite things are reading funny books and jumping in a pool with his kids: Sebastian, Lucia Lorraine, and his new baby boy, Carsten or "Mr. C."

Stephen received his medical degree from Georgetown University School of Medicine and his bachelor's from Harvard College.

Hans and Jen riding horses in the mountains of Costa Rica

Hans (age 10) and his childhood horse, Seradi

If you like this book, try:

For these and other Mister Lemur books and albums, visit www.LemurStore.com